It's Easy To Play Carpenters.

This book © Copyright 1979 by
Wise Publications
Exclusive distributors:
Music Sales Limited
8/9 Frith Street, London, W1V 5TZ, England
Music Sales Pty. Limited
120 Rothschild Avenue, Rosebery, NSW 2018, Australia

Compilation: Peter Evans
Arranger: Cyril Watters

Music Sales complete catalogue lists thousands of
titles and is free from your local music book shop,
or direct from Music Sales Limited.
Please send a cheque or Postal Order for £1·50 for postage to
Music Sales Limited, 8/9 Frith Street, London W1V 5TZ.

Printed in England by
Eyre & Spottiswoode Ltd, London and Margate.

Solitaire

Words and music by Neil Sedaka and Phil Cody.

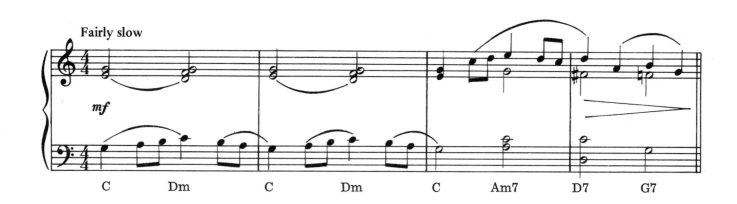

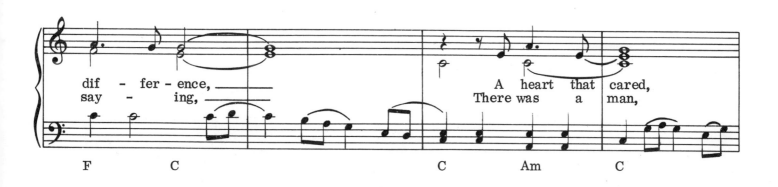

that went un - shared,
a lone - ly man,

Un - til it
Who would com-

Am

G

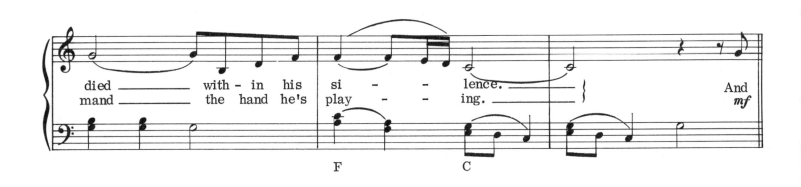

died _____ with - in his si - - lence. _____
mand _____ the hand he's play - - ing. _____

And
mf

F

C

Sol - i - taire's the on - ly game in town,

and ev'ry road that takes him, takes him

C

Am

down.

And by him - self it's ea - sy to pre - tend _____ he'll nev - er

F

Dm

G

love a - gain, _____

And keep - ing to him - self he plays the

F

C

C

game; with-out her love it al-ways ends the same. While

Am

life goes on a-round him ev'-ry where ___ he's play-ing Sol - i - taire. ___

F   Dm   G   F   C

Sol - i - taire ___ And Sol - i-taire's the on-ly game in

F   C   C

town, and ev' - ry road that takes him, takes him down. While

Am

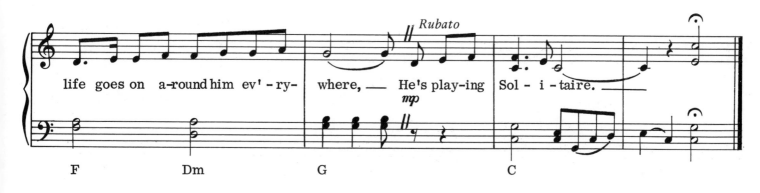

life goes on a-round him ev'-ry- where, ___ He's play-ing Sol - i - taire. ___

Rubato

mp

F   Dm   G   C

7

Let Me Be The One

Words by Paul Williams
Music by Roger Nichols

mf Let me be the one you run to, Let me be the one you come to when you

F   Em   A

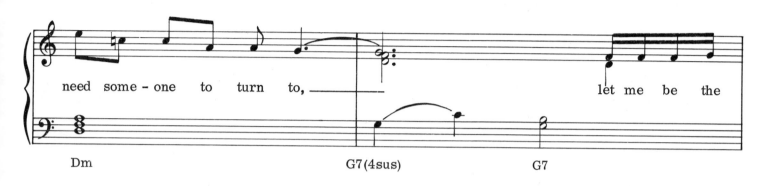

need some - one to turn to, _____ let me be the

Dm   G7(4sus)   G7

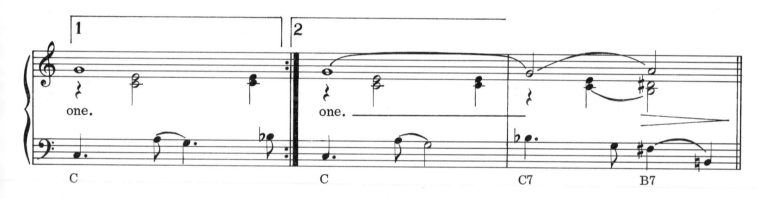

1 one.   **2** one. _____

C   C   C7   B7

mp For love and un - der - stand - ing,   to find a qui - et

E   C#m   D#m7   D   E7

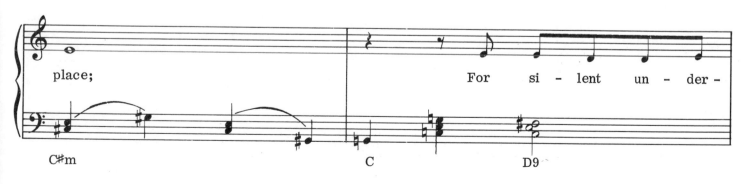

place;   For si - lent un - der -

C#m   C   D9

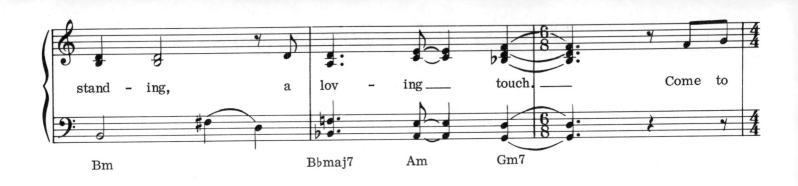

stand - ing, a lov - ing ___ touch. ___ Come to

Bm   B♭maj7   Am   Gm7

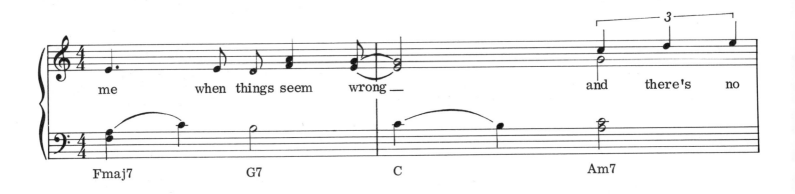

me when things seem wrong ___ and there's no

Fmaj7   G7   C   Am7

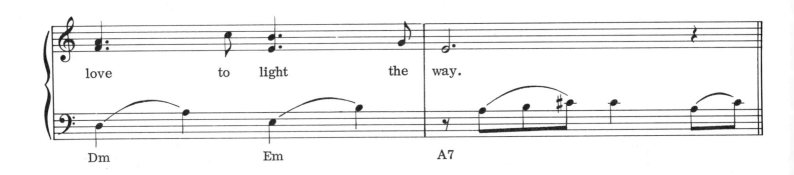

love to light the way.

Dm   Em   A7

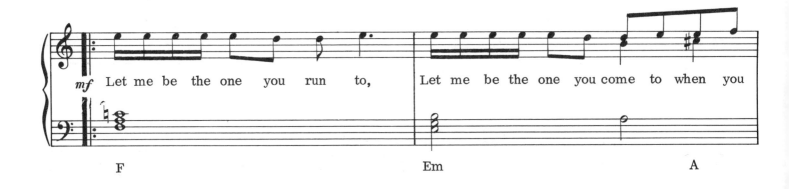

mf Let me be the one you run to, Let me be the one you come to when you

F   Em   A

Repeat and fade

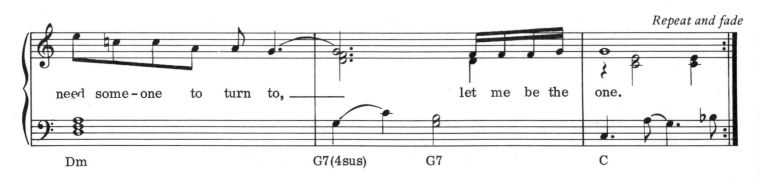

need some - one to turn to, ___ let me be the one.

Dm   G7(4sus)   G7   C

Please Mr. Postman

Words and music by B. Holland and F.C. Gorman

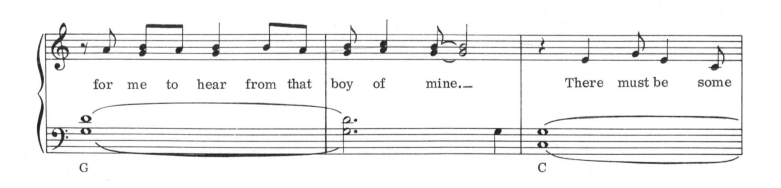

word to-day ____ From my boy-friend so far a-way.____

Am

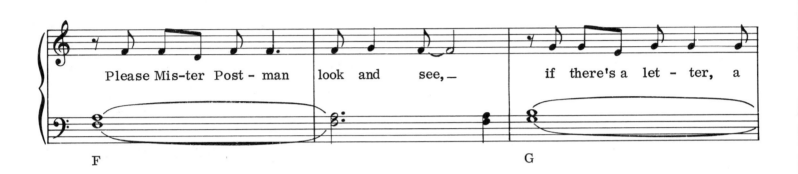

Please Mis-ter Post-man look and see, ___ if there's a let-ter, a

F   G

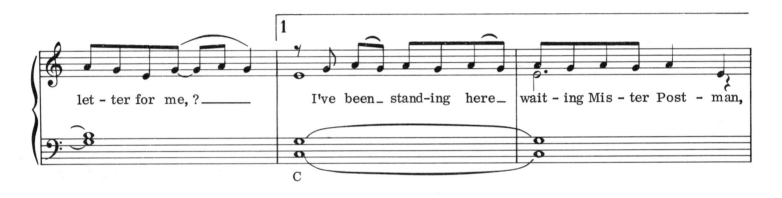

1

let-ter for me, ?____ I've been_ stand-ing here_ wait-ing Mis-ter Post-man,

C

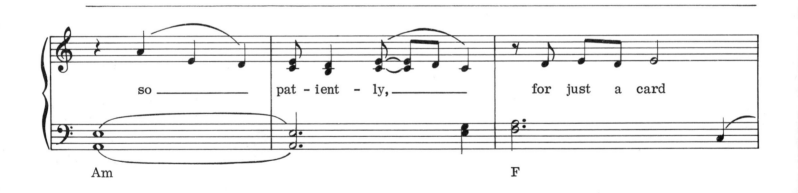

so _____ pat-ient-ly, _____ for just a card

Am   F

or just a let-ter say-ing he's re-turn-ing home_ to me.___ Mis-ter,

G

Mis - ter Post-man look and see,_ if there's a let-ter in your bag for me?_

C   Am

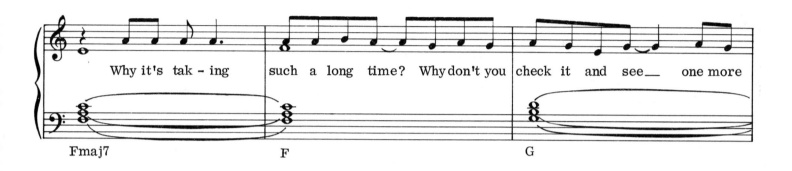

Why it's tak - ing such a long time? Why don't you check it and see_ one more

Fmaj7   F   G

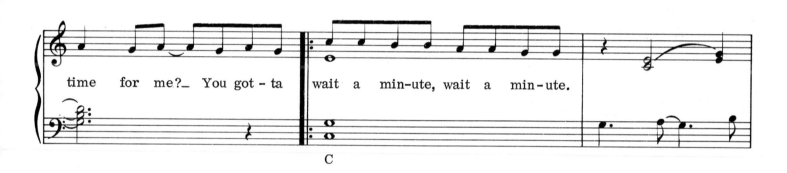

time for me?_ You got - ta wait a min-ute, wait a min-ute.

C

Wait a min-ute, wait a min-ute, Ooo_____ Mis - ter Post - man

Am   Fmaj7

Repeat and fade

look and see._ Come on de - liv - er the let - ter, the soon-er the bet - ter.____

G

Rainy Days And Mondays

Words by Paul Williams
Music by Roger Nichols

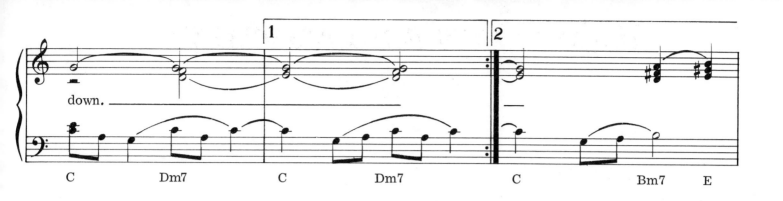

down.

C | Dm7 | C | Dm7 | C | Bm7 E

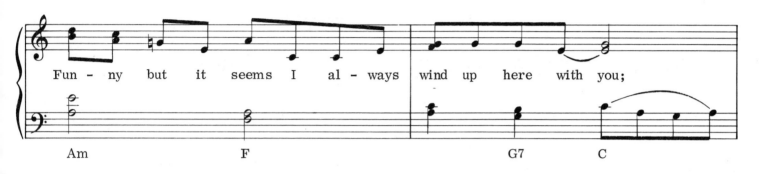

Fun — ny but it seems I al — ways wind up here with you;

Am | F | G7 | C

nice to know some bo - dy__ loves__ me,

Em | F | Dm | G7 | E

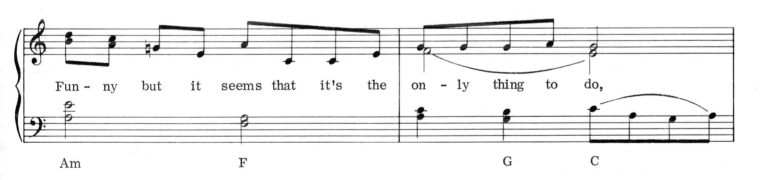

Fun — ny but it seems that it's the on - ly thing to do,

Am | F | G | C

D.S. al Coda 𝄋

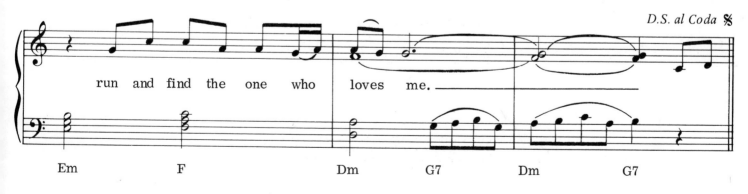

run and find the one who loves me.

Em | F | Dm | G7 | Dm | G7

⊕ CODA

down.   Hang - ing   a - round,

Em   Am   E Am   Fmaj7

noth - ing to do but frown.   Rain - y days and Mon - days al - ways get me —

Dm7   C   F   Dm Em F

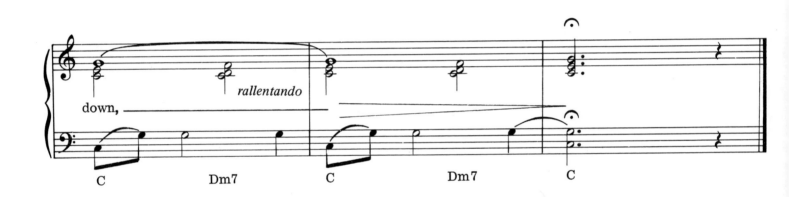

down, _____ *rallentando*

C   Dm7   C   Dm7   C

3. What I feel has come and gone before,
   No need to talk it out,
   We know what it's all about.
   Hangin' around, nothing to do but frown;
   Rainy Days and Mondays always get me down.

Hurting Each Other

Words by Peter Udell
Music by Gary Geld

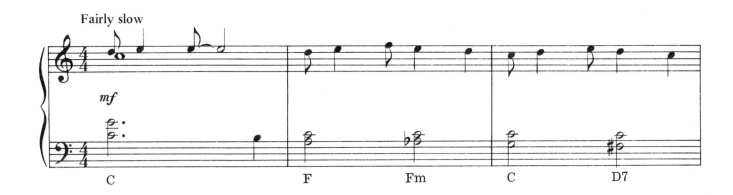

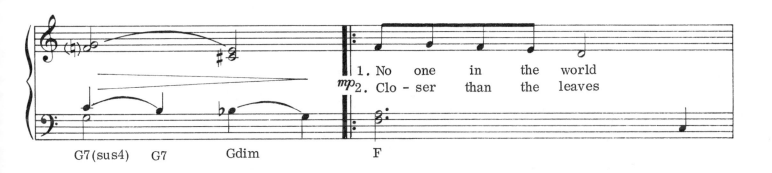

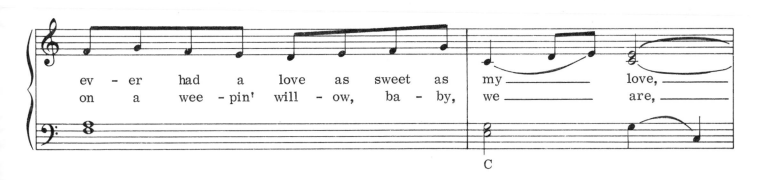

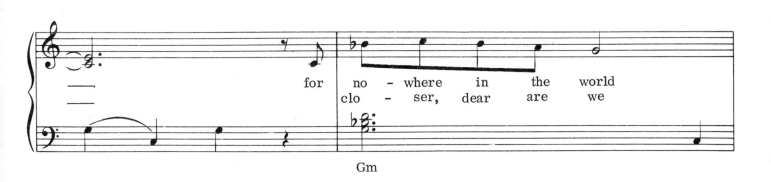

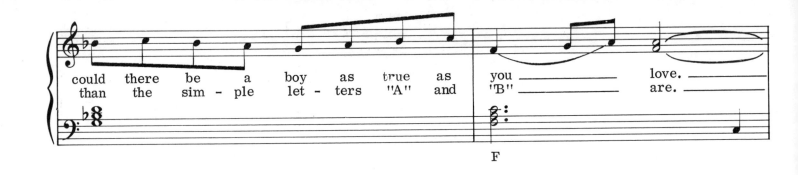

could there be a boy as true as you _____ love. _____
than the sim-ple let-ters "A" and "B" _____ are. _____

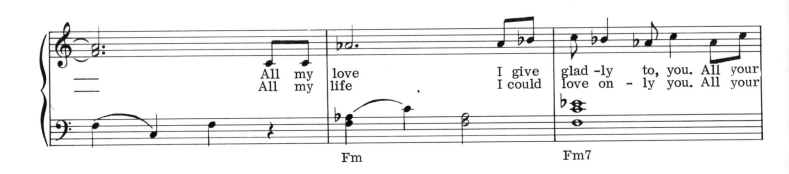

All my love I give glad-ly to, you. All your
All my life I could love on-ly you. All your

Fm   Fm7

love you give glad-ly to me. Tell me
life you could love on-ly me. Tell me

Cmaj7   D7

why then, oh why should it be that
why then, oh why should it be that

Fmaj7   C   F

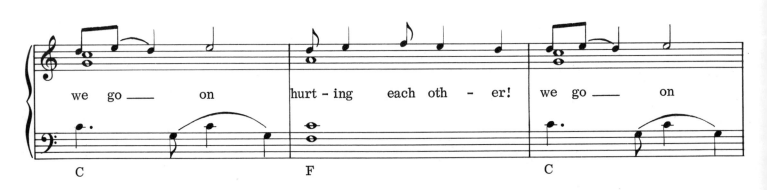

we go ____ on hurt-ing each oth-er! we go ____ on

C   F   C

Sing

Words and music by Joe Raposo

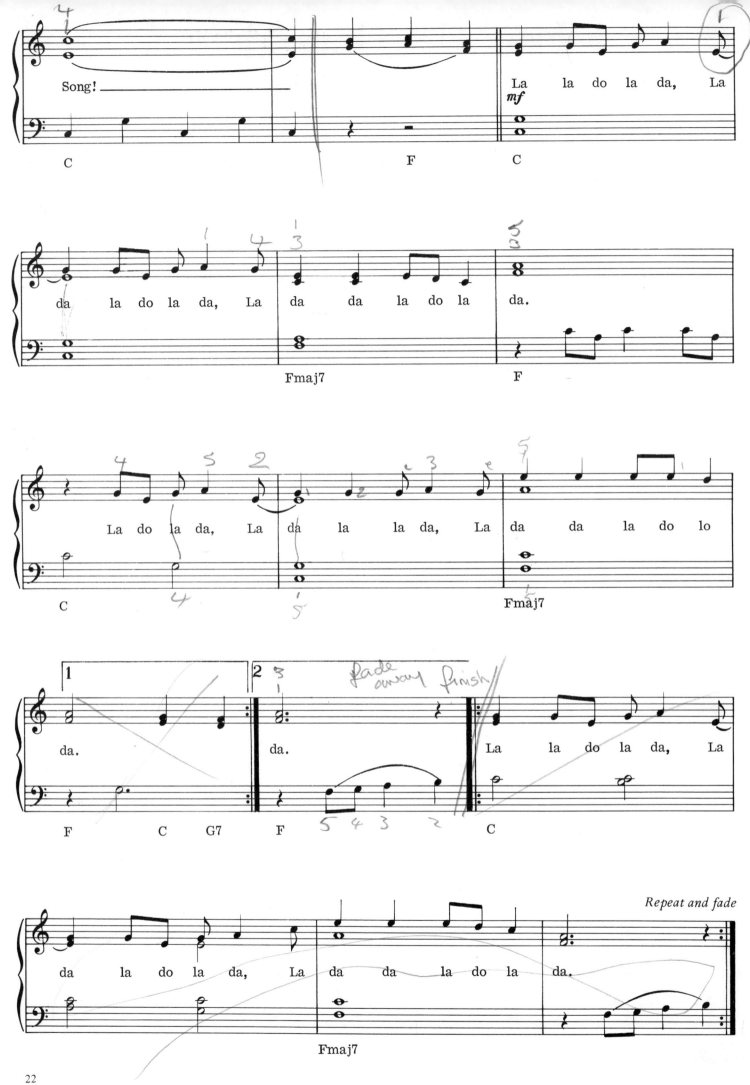

Yesterday Once More

Words and music by Richard Carpenter and John Bettis

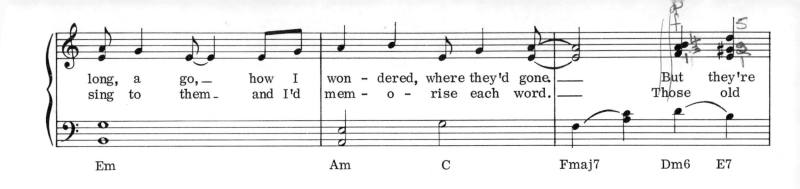

long, a go,— how I won-dered, where they'd gone.__ But they're
sing to them__ and I'd mem-o-rise each word.__ Those old

Em   Am   C   Fmaj7   Dm6   E7

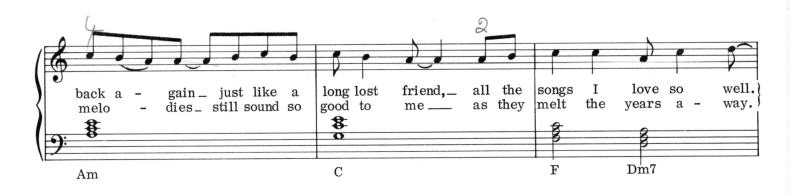

back a - gain__ just like a long lost friend,— all the songs I love so well.
melo - dies— still sound so good to me __ as they melt the years a - way.

Am   C   F   Dm7

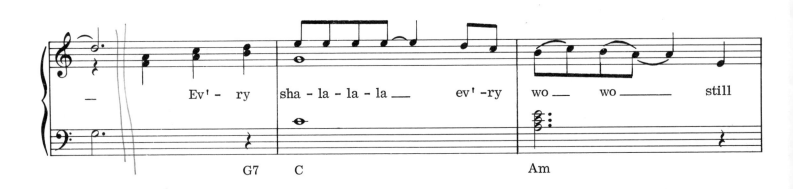

— Ev'-ry sha-la-la-la-la__ ev'-ry wo — wo ____ still

G7   C   Am

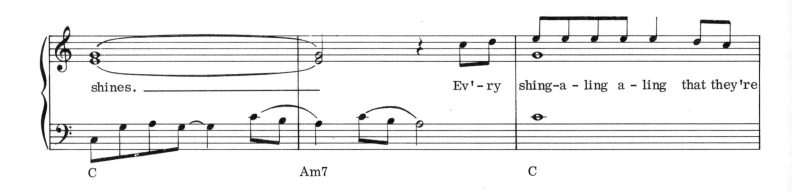

shines. _____ Ev'-ry shing-a-ling a-ling that they're

C   Am7   C

star-tin' to sing__ so fine, _____ When they
All my

Am   Dm7   G

get to the part___ where he's break-ing her heart,___ it can real - ly make me
best mem-or - ies___ come back clear-ly to me, ___ some can ev - en make me

Am   C+   C

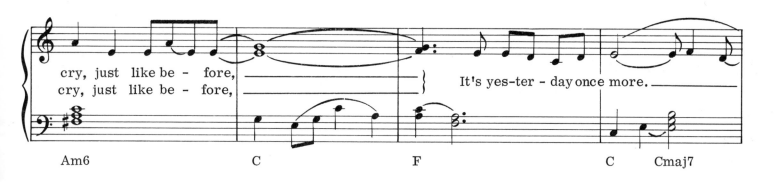

cry, just like be - fore, _____ It's yes-ter - day once more. ___
cry, just like be - fore, _____

Am6   C   F   C   Cmaj7

1

— (Shoo-bie do lang lang.)___ Look - in' ___

2

Ev' - ry

F6   Cmaj7   F6   F6   G

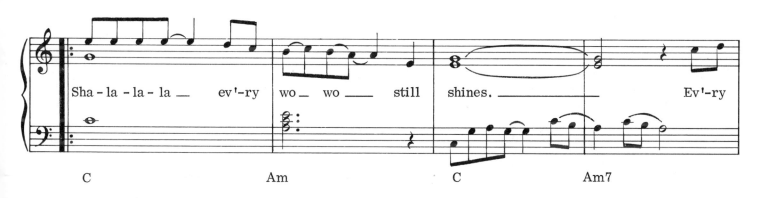

Sha - la - la - la ___ ev'-ry wo — wo ___ still shines. _____ Ev'-ry

C   Am   C   Am7

Repeat and fade

shing - a - ling-a-ling that they're startin' to sing___ so fine. _____ Ev' - ry

C   Am7   Dm7   G

Only Yesterday

Words by John Bettis
Music by Richard Carpenter

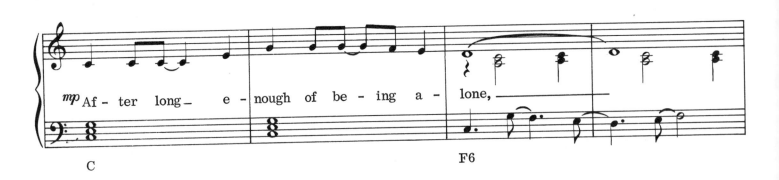

thru, and wait-in' was all_ my heart could do.___

F   Dm7   C   G

Hope was all_ I had un-til you came;___

C   D7

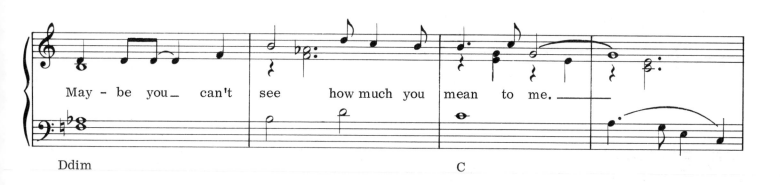

May - be you_ can't see how much you mean to me.___

Ddim   C

You were the dawn break-ing the night, the pro-mise of morn - ing

Am   D7   G   C

light, fil - ling the world,_ sur - round - ing me._ When I hold you,

F   D7   G7   F   G

Ba - by, ba - by, feels like may - be things will be all right.

Bb   Dm

Ba - by, ba - by, your love's made me free as a song,— sing-in' for-ev - er.

Bb   Dm7   G7   F   G7

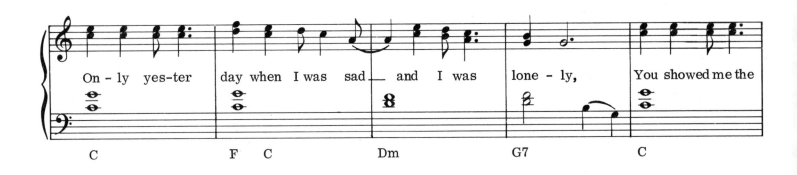

On - ly yes-ter day when I was sad— and I was lone - ly, You showed me the

C   F   C   Dm   G7   C

way to leave the past— and all its tears be-hind me. To-mor-row may be e -ven

F   C   Dm7   G   F   G   E   E7

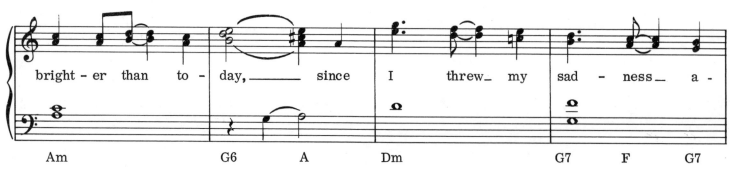

bright - er than to - day,_____ since I threw_ my sad - ness_ a-

Am   G6   A   Dm   G7   F   G7

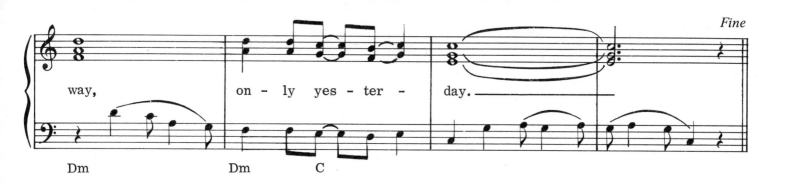

way, on - ly yes - ter - day. ____

Dm   Dm   C

I have found my home here in your arms, ____

C   F6

No - where else on earth I'd real - ly rath - er be. ____

Dm   G7   C

Life waits for us, share it with me. the best is a - bout to

Am   D7   G   Em

D.S. al fine 𝄋

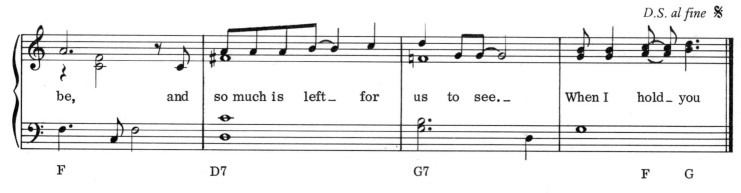

be, and so much is left for us to see. When I hold you

F   D7   G7   F   G

29

We've Only Just Begun

Words by Paul Williams
Music by Roger Nichols

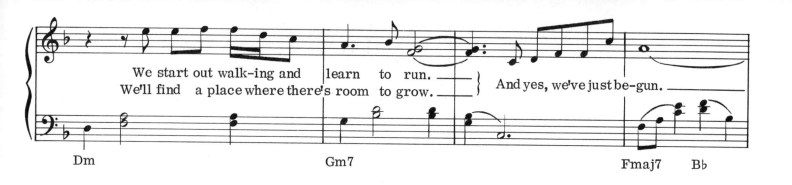

We start out walk-ing and learn to run.
We'll find a place where there's room to grow. And yes, we've just be-gun.

Dm   Gm7   Fmaj7   Bb

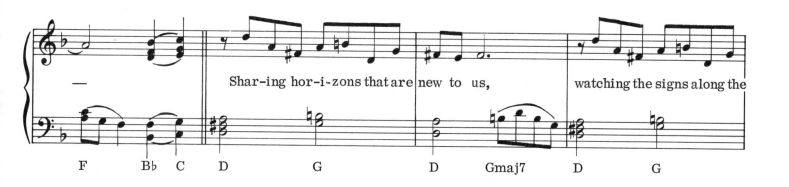

— Shar-ing hor-i-zons that are new to us, watching the signs along the

F   Bb   C   D   G   D   Gmaj7   D   G

way. Talk-ing it ov-er just the two of us, working to-geth-er, day to

D   Gmaj7   F#   B   F#   Bmaj7   F#   B

D.S. al Coda 𝄋

1   **2**

day, to-geth-er.___ geth-er, _____ to-geth-er.___

Gm7   (Gm7)   Gm7

𝄌 **CODA**

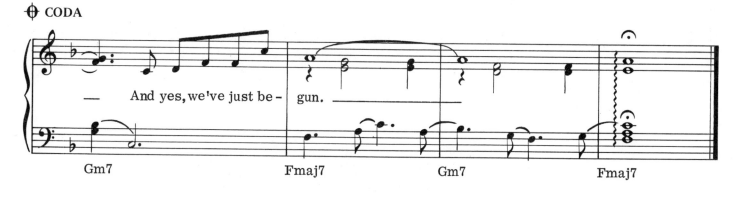

— And yes, we've just be- gun. _____

Gm7   Fmaj7   Gm7   Fmaj7

Top Of The World

Words by John Bettis
Music by Richard Carpenter

Moderato

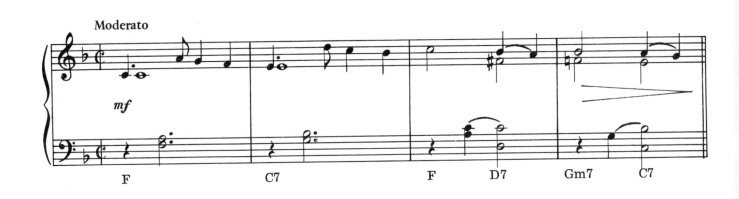

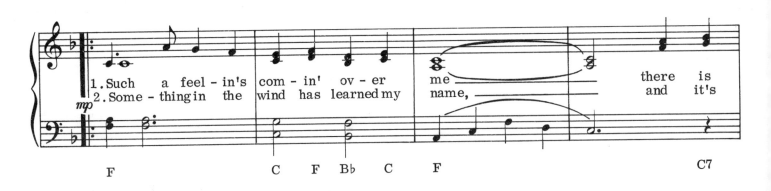

1. Such a feel-in's com-in' ov-er me, _____ there is
2. Some-thing in the wind has learned my name, _____ and it's

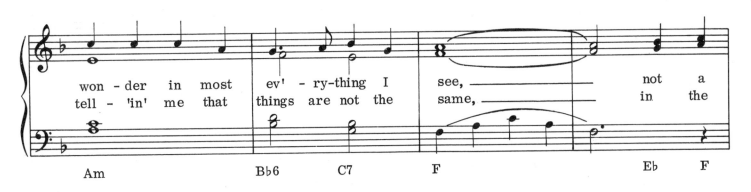

won - der in most ev' - ry-thing I see, _____ not a
tell - 'in' me that things are not the same, _____ in the

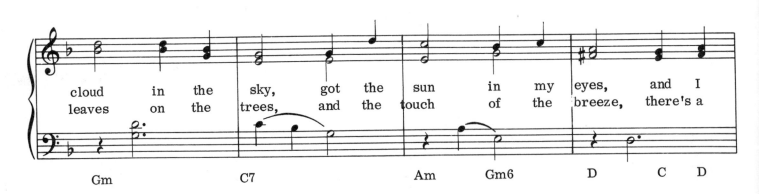

cloud in the sky, got the sun in my eyes, and I
leaves on the trees, and the touch of the breeze, there's a

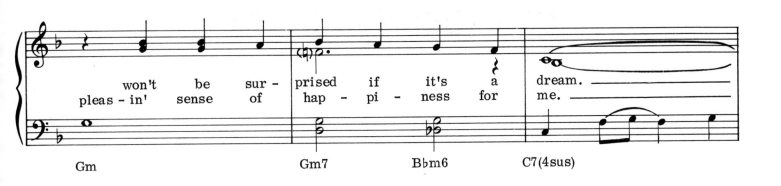

won't be sur - prised if it's a dream.
pleas - in' sense of hap - pi - ness for me.

Gm   Gm7   Bbm6   C7(4sus)

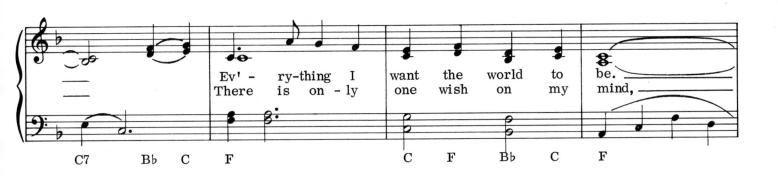

Ev' - ry-thing I want the world to be.
There is on - ly one wish on my mind,

C7   Bb   C   F   C   F   Bb   C   F

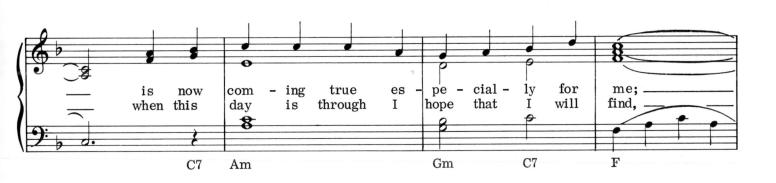

is now com - ing true es - pe - cial - ly for me;
when this day is through I hope that I will find,

C7   Am   Gm   C7   F

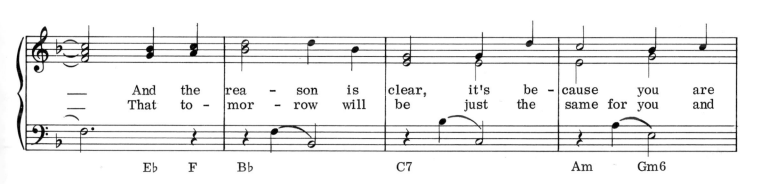

And the rea - son is clear, it's be - cause you are
That to - mor - row will be just the same for you and

Eb   F   Bb   C7   Am   Gm6

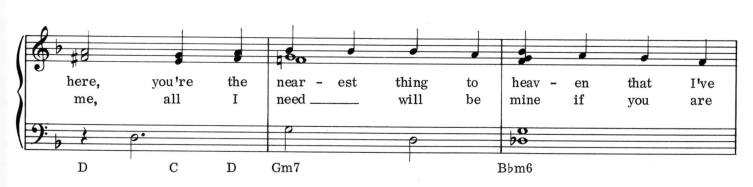

here, you're the near - est thing to heav - en that I've
me, all I need   will be mine if you are

D   C   D   Gm7   Bbm6

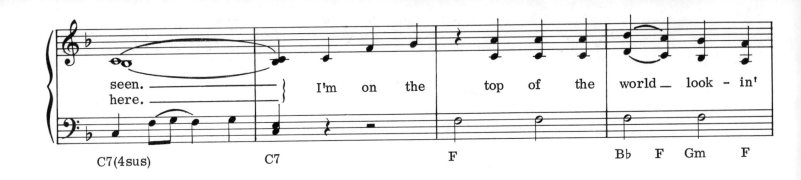

seen. _____ I'm on the top of the world_ look - in'

here. _____

C7(4sus)　　　　C7　　　　F　　　　Bb　F　Gm　F

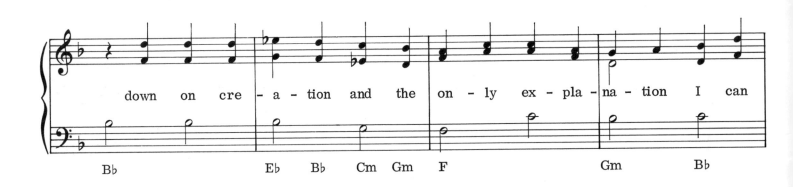

down on cre — a - tion and the on — ly ex — pla — na - tion I can

Bb　　　　Eb　Bb　Cm　Gm　F　　　　Gm　　　Bb

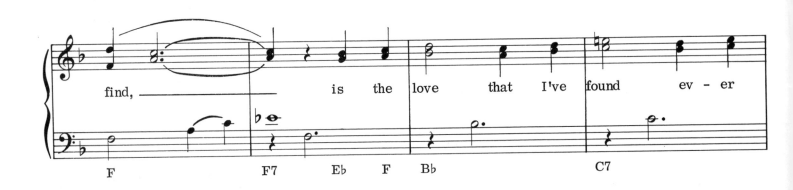

find, _____ is the love that I've found ev - er

F　　　　F7　　Eb　F　Bb　　　　C7

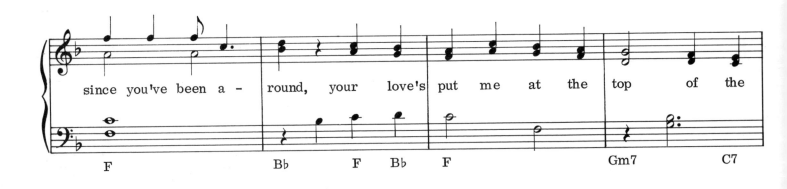

since you've been a - round, your love's put me at the top of the

F　　　　Bb　　F　Bb　F　　　　Gm7　　　C7

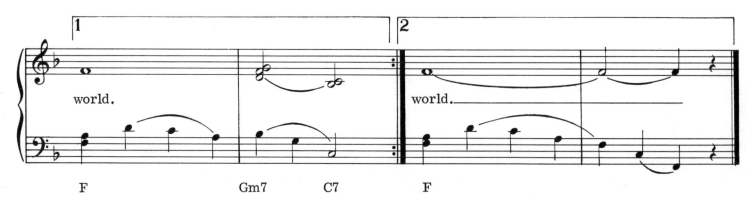

world.

world. _____

F　　　　Gm7　　C7　　　F

(They Long To Be) Close To You

Words by Hal David
Music by Burt Bacharach

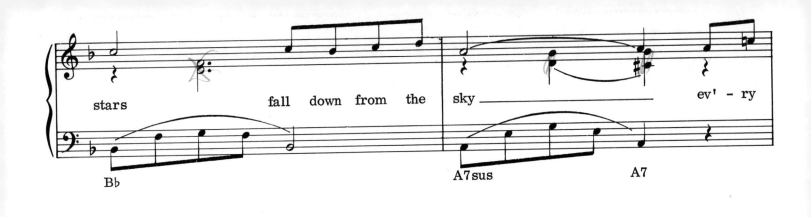

stars   fall down from the   sky _____ ev' - ry

Bb   A7sus   A7

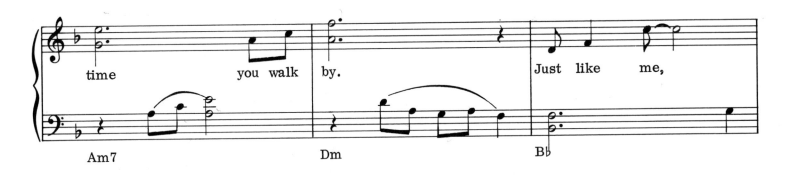

time   you walk   by.   Just like   me,

Am7   Dm   Bb

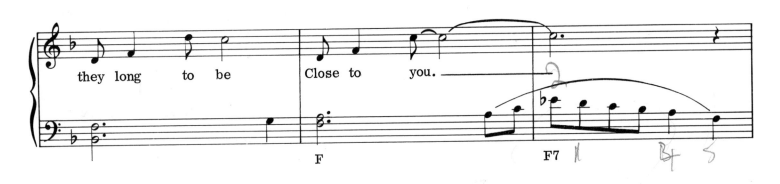

they long   to   be   Close to   you. _____

F   F7

On   the   day   that   you   were born   the   an - gels   got   to - geth - er   and   de -

Bb

- ci - ded   to   cre - ate   a   dream come   true. _____ So they

Am   D7

An Old Fashioned Love Song

Words & Music by Paul Williams

pro - mis - ing they'll nev - er go. ____

You'll swear you've heard ____

____ it be - fore ____ as it slow - ly ram - bles on and on. ____

No need in bring - ing 'em back ____ 'cause they've nev - er real - ly

gone.   Just an old fash - ioned

love song,   com-ing down __ in

three part har - mo - ny. ___

Just an   old   fash - ioned   love   song,

one, I'm   sure __ they wrote __   for   you and

me,   to weave our   dreams up - on __ and   lis - ten to __ each

To Coda

40

eve - ning   when the   lights ___ are low. ___

To un - der - score ___ our

love af - fair ___ with   ten - der - ness ___ and   feel - ings   that we've

come to know. ___

D.%. al Coda   ✛ **CODA**   Bb tacet

me.

sfz

41

For All We Know

Words by Robb Wilson and Arthur James
Music by Fred Karlin

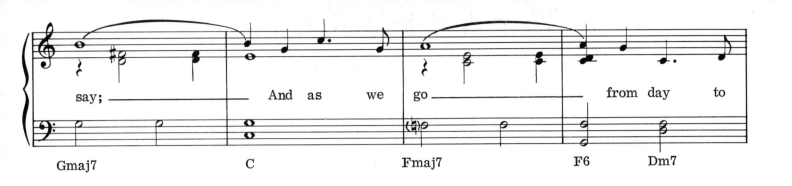

say; _____ And as we go _____ from day to

Gmaj7   C   Fmaj7   F6   Dm7

day. _____ I'll feel you close to me, _____ to
two of us, _____

C   D7

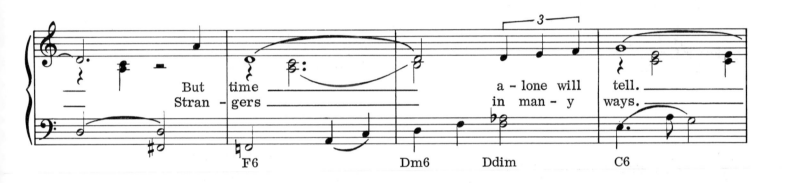

But time _____ a - lone will tell. _____
Stran - gers _____ in man - y ways. _____

F6   Dm6   Ddim   C6

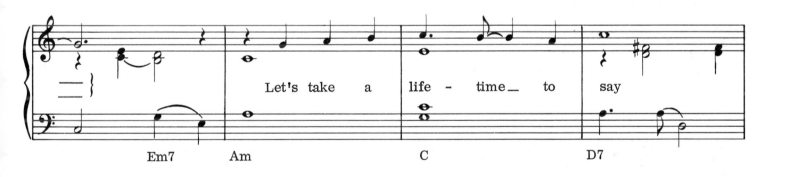

Let's take a life - time to say

Em7   Am   C   D7

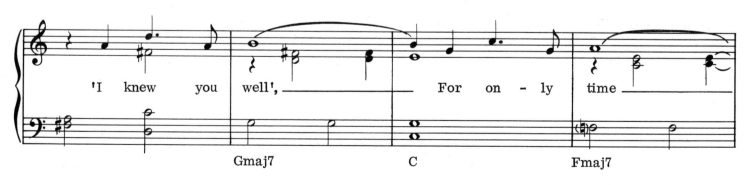

'I knew you well', _____ For on - ly time _____

Gmaj7   C   Fmaj7

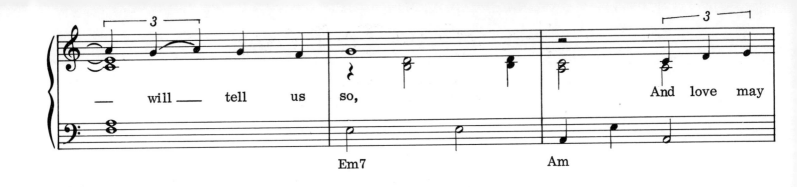

will ___ tell us so,

Em7

Am

And love may

grow for all ___ we know

Fmaj7

G7

F

C

Am7

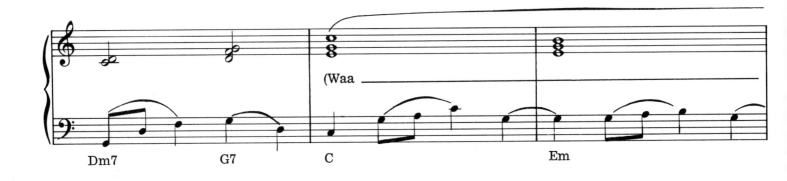

(Waa ___

Dm7

G7

C

Em

Love, ___

Dm

G7

1

C

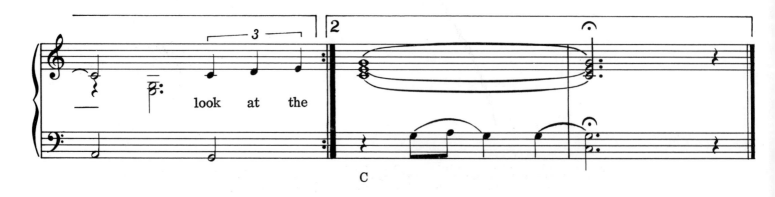

look at the

2

C

Goodbye To Love

Words by John Bettis
Music by Richard Carpenter

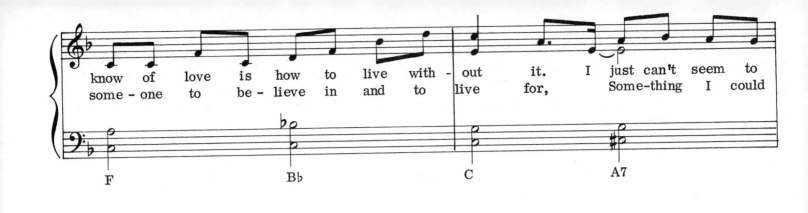

know of love is how to live with - out it. I just can't seem to
some - one to be - lieve in and to live it for, Some-thing I could

F   Bb   C   A7

find it.
live for,

So I've made my mind up I must
All the years of use - less search have
What lies in the fut - ure is a

Dm   Dm6   F   C7

live my life a - lone, And
fin - 'lly reached an end.
mys - t'ry to us all,

tho' it's not the eas - y way I
Lone - li - ness, and, emp - ty days will
No one can pre - dict the wheel of

F   Gm7   F   Gm7

1
guess I've al - ways known I'd say good-

2
be my on - ly friend, From this

F   Gm7   F   Gm7

day love is for - got - ten, I'll go on as best I can. I'll say good-

Am7   D7   Bbm6   Gm7   C7

for-tune as it falls. There may come a time when I will see that I've been wrong. But for

F   Gm7   F   Gm7   F   Gm7

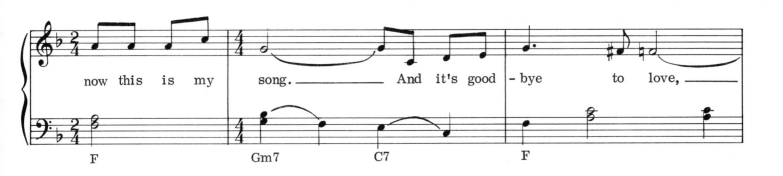

now this is my song. _____ And it's good - bye to love, _____

F   Gm7   C7   F

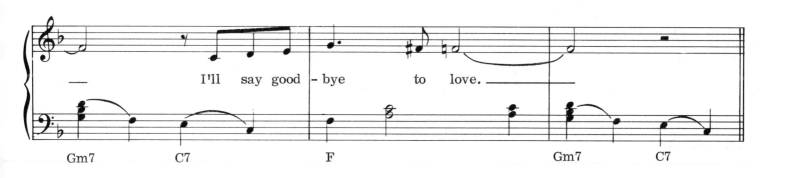

— I'll say good - bye to love. _____

Gm7   C7   F   Gm7   C7

Ah _____

F   Am   F7   Bb6   Bbm   F   Dm6   C

Repeat and fade

Ah _____

F   Am   F7   Bb6   Bbm   F   Bb   C   F